Success

Assessment Papers

More Maths

age 10 – 11 · levels 4 – 5

Steve Hobbs

Sample page

paper number for
quick reference

level showing
attainment target

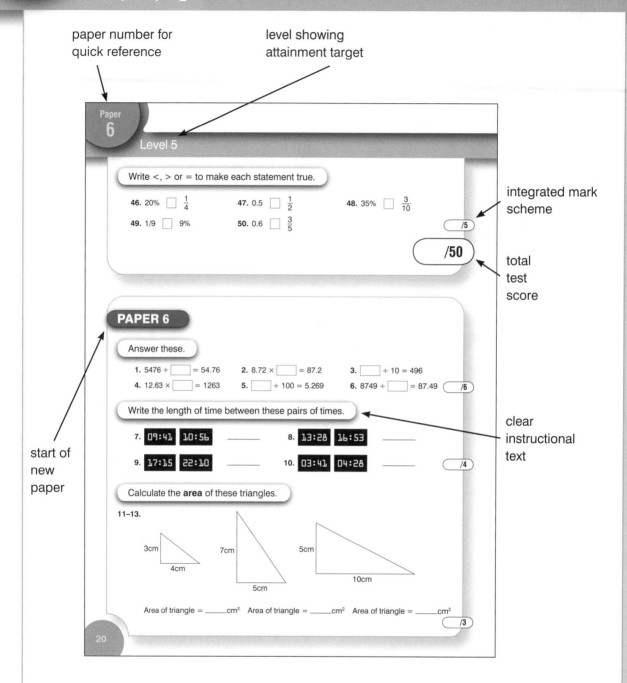

Paper 6

Level 5

Write <, > or = to make each statement true.

46. 20% ☐ $\frac{1}{4}$ **47.** 0.5 ☐ $\frac{1}{2}$ **48.** 35% ☐ $\frac{3}{10}$

49. 1/9 ☐ 9%   **50.** 0.6 ☐ $\frac{3}{5}$ /5

/**50**

integrated mark scheme

total test score

PAPER 6

Answer these.

1. 5476 ÷ ☐ = 54.76   **2.** 8.72 × ☐ = 87.2   **3.** ☐ ÷ 10 = 496

4. 12.63 × ☐ = 1263   **5.** ☐ ÷ 100 = 5.269   **6.** 8749 ÷ ☐ = 87.49   /6

Write the length of time between these pairs of times.

7. 09:41 10:56 _____   **8.** 13:28 16:53 _____

9. 17:15 22:10 _____   **10.** 03:41 04:28 _____   /4

clear instructional text

Calculate the **area** of these triangles.

11–13.

3cm
4cm

7cm
5cm

5cm
10cm

Area of triangle = _____cm²   Area of triangle = _____cm²   Area of triangle = _____cm²

/3

start of new paper

20

2

Contents

PAPER 1

Answer these.

1. Two pairs of shoes cost £86 and £94. Circle the total cost.

    a) £169   **b)** £190   **c)** £180   **d)** £170

/1

2–7. Complete this multiplication grid.

×	3	8	___
___	9	24	18
4		32	
7		56	

/6

8–9. Circle the two **prime numbers** in the list.

    23   24   25   26   27   28   29

/2

10. What is the missing number? Circle the correct answer.

    $28 = 15 + (20 - \square)$

    a) 13   **b)** 7   **c)** 9   **d)** 15

/1

11–13. Round these football crowd sizes to the nearest 100.

    Manchester United   67 349 _____

    Chelsea   35 681 _____

    Arsenal   39 650 _____

/3

14. Put these fractions in order, starting with the smallest.

    $\frac{4}{10}$ $\frac{3}{8}$ $\frac{5}{6}$ $\frac{2}{3}$

/1

15–20. Convert these measurements to centimetres.

    3.5 metres _____cm   6.25 metres _____cm   8.75 metres _____cm

    12.5 metres _____cm   0.25 metres _____cm   20.75 metres _____cm

/6

Use a **protractor** to measure these angles.

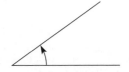  

21. _____ °   **22.** _____ °   **23.** _____ °   /3

Write these times as 24-hour clock times.

24. `10.50am` → _____   **25.** `5.10pm` → _____

26. `9.15am` → _____   **27.** `8.43pm` → _____   /4

Answer these.

28. Jack cycles 23 miles on Monday and double that distance on Tuesday.

How far in total does he cycle on both days? _____

29. Bradley buys concert tickets at £65 per ticket.

If he buys 6 tickets, how much does he spend in total? _____

30. Jodie is walking up stairs in a tall building. Each flight of stairs has 14 stairs and she walks up 6 flights.

How many stairs does she walk up in total? _____

31. Sarah puts a fence around her rectangular field. Two sides are 48 metres and 26 metres.

What is the **perimeter** of the field? _____   /4

32. What fraction of this shape is shaded?

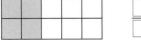

/1

33.

```
  4 8 6 3
+ 2 8 9 6
_____
```

34.

```
  8 5 4 2
- 5 2 6 9
_____
```

35.

```
  1 8 9 2
+ 5 9 8 2
_____
```

36.

```
  8 6 2 6
- 7 2 3 5
_____
```

/4

Look at these shapes. Read the description and select the shape.

| A | B | C | D |

37. Contains only 1 right angle. _____

38. Contains 2 acute angles and 2 obtuse angles. _____

39. Contains 4 right angles and 4 equal sides. _____

40. Contains 4 right angles and 2 pairs of sides of equal length. _____

/4

Answer these.

41. $248 \div 4 =$ _____ **42.** $366 \div 6 =$ _____ **43.** $824 \div 4 =$ _____ **44.** $402 \div 6 =$ _____   /4

45. $3x + 9 = 27$ $x =$ _____ **46.** $5y - 6 = 14$ $y =$ _____ **47.** $8z - 11 = 37$ $z =$ _____   /3

Write the amount of water in each jug as millilitres and litres.

48.

_____ml = _____ litres

49.

_____ml = _____ litres

50.

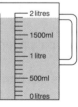

_____ml = _____ litres

/3

/50

PAPER 2

Answer these.

1–4. Write these decimals as fractions.

0.7   0.3   0.09   0.67

/4

5. Count forward in 10s → 6435 _____ _____ _____ 6475

6. Count back in 10s → 8776 _____ _____ _____ 8736

7. Count forward in 100s → 8949 _____ _____ _____ 9349

8. Count back in 100s → 4216 _____ _____ _____ 3816

/4

Look at these price tags and answer the questions.

Bicycle £119.00   **Mobile phone** £112.45   **Satnav** £168.30   **Suitcase** £89.99

9. What is the combined cost of the bicycle and satnav? _____

10. How much more does the mobile phone cost than the suitcase? _____

11. If Raj has £200, how much money will he have left if he buys the satnav? _____

/3

Answer these.

12–15. Write each of these four numbers in the correct places on this Venn diagram.

6   9   14   17

/4

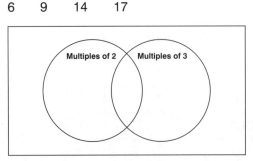

16–19. Write <, > or = to make each statement true.

8 × 7 ☐ 9 × 6   12 × 3 ☐ 9 × 4

84 ÷ 12 ☐ 64 ÷ 8   121 ÷ 11 ☐ 132 ÷ 12

/4

20. What is the **mean** of this group of numbers? _____

14   18   21   13   19

/1

In a bag there are 8 red balls and 4 blue balls. What is the **probability** of choosing the following? Choose your answers from the possibilities listed below.

1     $\frac{2}{3}$ $\frac{1}{3}$ 0

21. a red ball _____   **22.** a blue ball _____

23. a green ball _____   **24.** a red ball or a blue ball _____

/4

Write the next numbers in these **sequences**.

25. 786   789   792   795   798   _____   _____   _____

26. 386   379   372   365   358   _____   _____   _____

27. -13   -7   -1   _____   _____   _____

28. 9   -1   -11   _____   _____   _____

/4

Answer these.

29. A film starts at 25 past 7 and finishes at 10 past 9. How long does the film last?

_____

/1

30–33. Write the missing numbers going in and out of this function machine.

IN	6	9		
OUT			69	49

/4

Write the missing **digits**.

34. 5 7 2 ☐
     – 3 4 ☐ 8
     _____
        2 ☐ 6 1

35. ☐ 2 1 8
     – 6 ☐ 4 9
     _____
        1 9 ☐ 9

/2

Look at the grid.

36–38. Plot the points (-2, 1), (1, 3) and (0, 5) on the grid.

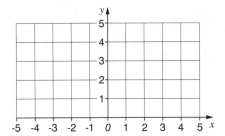

39. These points are the **vertices** of a parallelogram. Plot the fourth **vertex** and draw the shape.

40. What are the **coordinates** of the fourth vertex of the parallelogram? _____ /5

Answer these.

41–42. What is the **area** and **perimeter** of this shape?

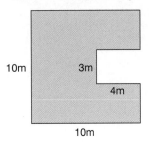

10m   3m
              4m

10m

Area = _____

Perimeter = _____   /2

43. Circle the number that is nearest to 12.

     12.5   12.25   11.96   12.05   11.99   /1

44. A new laptop usually costs £350. Today it has 30% off the price.

How much does the laptop cost today? _____

/1

Use these numbers to answer the questions.

| 39 | 56 | 47 | 83 | 21 |

45. Which two numbers add up to 95? _____ _____

46. Which two numbers divide exactly by 3? _____ _____

47. Which number is the **product** of 8 and 7? _____

48. Which two numbers have a **difference** of 36? _____ _____

49. Which number is in the 2 times tables? _____

50. Which three numbers have a
remainder of 3 when divided by 4? _____ _____ _____

/6

/50

PAPER 3

Answer these.

1. Circle two numbers that are **multiples** of 8.

12   15   24   34   48   62   94

/1

2. Draw any lines of **symmetry**
on the triangle.

/1

3. Write these weights in order, starting with the smallest.

780g   45g   7.9kg   78g   4.5kg   78kg   7800g   /1

_____   _____   _____   _____   _____   _____   _____

4–5. On this grid draw a rectangle with an **area** of 30 squares and a **perimeter** of 22 squares.

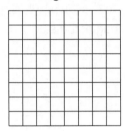

/2

6–9. Complete these.

_____ × 10 = 13.63   27.63 × _____ = 2763

_____ ÷ 10 = 20.01   98.76 ÷ _____ = 0.9876   /4

10–13. Write these fractions in their simplest form.

$\frac{6}{9} = \frac{\square}{\square}$ $\frac{20}{25} = \frac{\square}{\square}$ $\frac{8}{18} = \frac{\square}{\square}$ $\frac{25}{100} = \frac{\square}{\square}$ /4

14. I am thinking of a number. If I take away 7 from it and then multiply by 5, the answer is 55.

What number am I thinking of? _____   /1

15. How many **edges** does a square-based pyramid have? Circle the correct answer.

4   6   8   2   /1

16–21. Write the missing numbers on this addition grid.

+	76	43	62
32			94
56		99	
83	159		

/6

22–27. Insert brackets to make each number sentence correct.

27 ÷ 12 − 3 = 3   6 × 5 ÷ 3 = 10   36 ÷ 2 + 4 = 6

8 × 6 + 2 = 50   4 + 4 × 5 = 24   12 − 8 ÷ 2 = 2   /6

Answer these.

28. In a class of 24 children, $\frac{3}{8}$ of the class is girls.

How many of the children are girls? _____

29. Daniel eats $\frac{4}{10}$ of a bag of sweets. There were 50 sweets in the bag at the start.

How many sweets does Daniel eat? _____

30. Lauren has £96 and spends $\frac{2}{3}$ of her money on books.

How much does she spend on books? _____

31. In a building with 25 flights of stairs, Kim is $\frac{2}{5}$ of the way up.

How many flights of stairs has he completed? _____

32. In a football season, Jared's football team won $\frac{3}{4}$ of their games. They played 32 games in total.

How many games did they win? _____

/5

Read these scales and write each weight in grams and kilograms.

33.

_____g = _____kg

34.

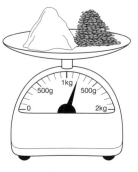

_____g = _____kg

35.

_____g = _____kg

/3

This graph shows the distance in metres run by four children in 1 minute.

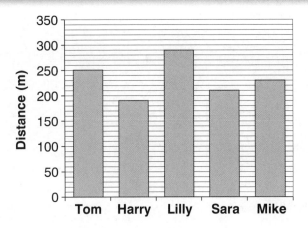

36. Who ran the furthest? _____

37. How much further did Sara run than Harry? _____

38. Who finished 20 metres in front of Sara? _____

39. Write the children in order starting with the person who ran the furthest.

_____

/4

Answer these.

40. What is the **product** of 9 and 7? _____

41. There are two **square numbers** between 42 and 72.
What is the **difference** between these two numbers? _____

42. What is the sum of 56, 38 and 74? _____

/3

Find the **median** and **mode** of these sets of numbers.

43–46. 57, 28, 45, 18, 86, 45, 26, 45, 8, 86   Median = _____ Mode = _____

130, 105, 111, 109, 130, 111, 126, 126, 130, 127   Median = _____ Mode = _____   /4

Look at the shapes. Write the **probability** of choosing the shapes listed in the questions.

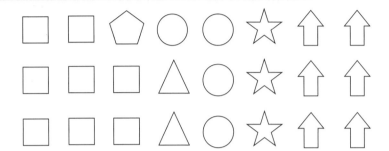

47. The probability of choosing a triangle is _____

48. The probability of choosing an arrow is _____

49. The probability of choosing a square is _____

50. The probability of choosing a circle or a star is _____

/4

/50

PAPER 4

Write the next numbers in these **sequences**.

1. 57   38   19   _____   _____

2. 27   13   -1   _____   _____

3. -29   -6   17   _____   _____

4. 9   -7   -23   _____   _____

/4

Round these numbers to one decimal place.

5–10. 16.58 _____   21.86 _____   14.23 _____

10.15 _____   26.60 _____   16.78 _____

/6

Answer these.

11. Put these **negative** temperatures in order, coldest to warmest.

-11°C   -3°C   -14°C   -1°C   -19°C

Coldest _____   _____   _____   _____   _____ Warmest

/1

12–13. Circle two **prime numbers** from the numbers below.

24   25   29   32   34   37   39

/2

14–19. Write these fractions as decimals.

$\dfrac{2}{5}$ _____ $\dfrac{3}{4}$ _____ $\dfrac{6}{20}$ _____

$\dfrac{14}{25}$ _____ $\dfrac{16}{50}$ _____ $\dfrac{8}{25}$ _____

/6

20. $10 - 4.7 =$ ⬚   **21.** $10 - 1.1 =$ ⬚   **22.** $10 - 0.6 =$ ⬚

23. $100 - 24.7 =$ ⬚   **24.** $100 - 72.6 =$ ⬚   **25.** $100 - 8.5 =$ ⬚

/6

26. The **ratio** of boys to girls in a school is 5:3. There are 248 children in the school.

How many boys are in school? _____

/1

27–29. Find the value of x.

$3x - 20 = 4$ $8 + 2x = 20$ $3 - 9x = -24$

$x =$ _____ $x =$ _____ $x =$ _____

/3

30. What are the **coordinates** of the rectangle?

(⬚ , ⬚), (⬚ , ⬚), (⬚ , ⬚), (⬚ , ⬚),

/1

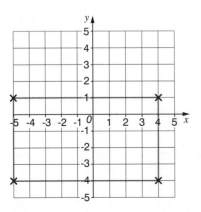

Write the missing angle for each of these.

31.

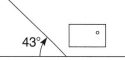

43°

32.

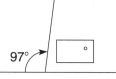

97°

/2

Answer these.

33. 2.5kg + 40g = _____

34. 1.8 litres + 25ml = _____

35. 3.4km + 75m = _____

36. 2.7kg + 7g = _____

37. 5.4 litres + 125ml = _____

38. 4.1km + 2m = _____

/6

39. From a science experiment, the following temperatures were recorded.

   9°C   12°C   10°C   8°C   13°C   8°C

   What is the **mean** temperature? _____

/1

40–43. What is the **area** and **perimeter** of these rectangles?

12cm

4cm

23cm

6cm

Rectangle A

Rectangle B

Area = _____

Area = _____

Perimeter = _____

Perimeter = _____

/4

44–47.   823   482   613   440
           × 35   × 13   × 24   × 20
         _____   _____   _____   _____

/4

48–50. 188 ÷ 4 = _____   324 ÷ 6 = _____   576 ÷ 8 = _____

/3

/50

PAPER 5

Calculate these amounts.

1. 50% of 240ml _____

2. 5% of 80kg _____

3. 80% of 60cm _____

4. 35% of 120m _____

5. 95% of 150mm _____

6. 25% of 24km _____

/6

Answer these.

7–12. Round these amounts of money to the nearest 10p.

£8.63 _____   £9.25 _____   £11.50 _____

£10.95 _____   £13.01 _____   £14.44 _____

/6

13. Which two **prime numbers** multiply to make 437?

☐ × ☐ = 437

/1

Write the missing angle for each of these.

14.

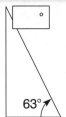

15.

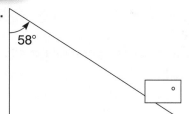

/2

Complete these sentences by writing the most sensible measurement from the options in the boxes.

| 4m | 10 litres | 70kg | 5kg | 300ml | 1m |

16–21. The man's leg is _____ long.

The length of the car is _____ long.

A can of cola holds about _____ of liquid.

The bag of potatoes weighs _____.

The watering can holds _____ of water.

The man weighs _____.   /6

Answer these.

22. Which distance in kilometres is **equivalent** to 20 miles (1 mile = 1.6 kilometres)? Circle the correct answer.

16km   20km   30km   32km   40km   /1

23–25. Find the value of the following **expressions** if $a = 12$.

$(5a - 20) + 6 = \boxed{}$ $(28 - 2a) + 6 = \boxed{}$ $3a - (36 - 18) = \boxed{}$ /3

26. This rectangle has a **perimeter** of 42cm. What is the length? _____   /1

8cm

Look at the shape.

27. What is the perimeter of the shape? _____   /1

28. What is the **area** of the shape? _____   /1

4cm

4cm

2cm

6cm

Solve these problems.

29. The table shows the number of goals scored by a footballer over 5 seasons.

Season 1	Season 2	Season 3	Season 4	Season 5
24	22	14	19	21

What is the **mean** number of goals he scores per season? _____

/1

30. A farmer keeps chicken and geese in the **ratio** of 7:4.

If he has 217 chickens, how many geese does he have? _____

/1

31. Paula drives a total of 435 miles during Saturday and Sunday. The ratio of miles driven on Saturday to Sunday is 3:2.

How far does she drive on Saturday? _____ miles

/1

Look at the Venn diagram.

32–39. Write these numbers in the correct places on this Venn diagram.

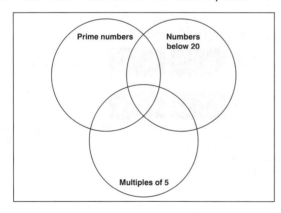

| 3 | 5 | 6 | 7 |

| 10 | 23 | 25 | 26 |

Prime numbers

Numbers below 20

Multiples of 5

/8

40–45. In a school children are asked which subject they prefer. There are 196 children in the school. 53 boys prefer Art. Use this information to complete the table.

	Music	Art	Total
Boys			102
Girls	48		
Total			196

/6

19

Write <, > or = to make each statement true.

46. 20% ☐ $\frac{1}{4}$ **47.** 0.5 ☐ $\frac{1}{2}$ **48.** 35% ☐ $\frac{3}{10}$

49. $\frac{1}{9}$ ☐ 9%   **50.** 0.6 ☐ $\frac{3}{5}$

/5

/50

PAPER 6

Answer these.

1. 5476 ÷ ☐ = 54.76   **2.** 8.72 × ☐ = 87.2   **3.** ☐ ÷ 10 = 496

4. 12.63 × ☐ = 1263   **5.** ☐ ÷ 100 = 5.269   **6.** 8749 ÷ ☐ = 87.49

/6

Write the length of time between these pairs of times.

7. `09:41` `10:56` _____   **8.** `13:28` `16:53` _____

9. `17:15` `22:10` _____   **10.** `03:41` `04:28` _____

/4

Calculate the **area** of these triangles.

11–13.

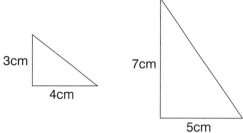

Area of triangle = _____cm²   Area of triangle = _____cm²   Area of triangle = _____cm²

/3

Answer these.

14–19. Write these fractions as **percentages**.

$\dfrac{1}{2}$ _____ $\dfrac{9}{10}$ _____ $\dfrac{18}{25}$ _____

$\dfrac{3}{5}$ _____ $\dfrac{1}{4}$ _____ $\dfrac{35}{50}$ _____   /6

20–22. Find the value of y.

$17 - 20y = -3$ $5y + 24 = 19$ $31 = 3y - 2$

$y = $ _____ $y = $ _____ $y = $ _____   /3

23. Which one of these distances in miles is **equivalent** to 50 kilometres (1 mile = 1.6 kilometres)? Circle the correct answer.

20 miles   25 miles   30 miles   35 miles   40 miles   /1

Answer these questions on **square numbers** and **square roots**.

24. What is $\sqrt{100}$? _____   **25.** What is 9^2? _____

26. What is $\sqrt{144}$? _____

27. Which two numbers when squared have a sum of 100? _____ and _____   /4

Look at the grid.

28. Find the **coordinates** of the fourth **vertex** of a parallelogram whose other three **vertices** are (4, 2), (6, 5) and (2, 5).

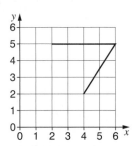

Fourth vertex _____   /1

What is the angle marked x in each shape?

29.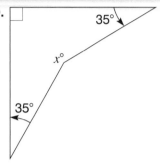

30.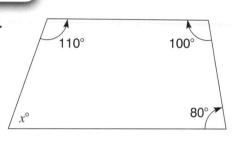

Angle x = _____

Angle x = _____

/2

Answer these.

31. I am thinking of a number. If I add 10 to the number and then divide it by 2 the answer is 9.

What number am I thinking of? _____

/1

32.   3 5 . 6 7

        ×   4
    _____

    _____

33.   2 3 . 2 3

        ×   5
    _____

    _____

34.   5 7 . 0 3

        ×   3
    _____

    _____

/3

35. What is the **perimeter** of this

isosceles triangle? _____

/1

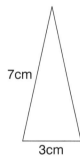

7cm

3cm

Solve these problems.

36. At the cinema, an orange juice and a box of popcorn cost £5.60. Two orange juices and a box of popcorn cost £7.50.

How much does a box of popcorn cost?   £ _____

37. A rail ticket for an adult costs £11.50 and a child's is half the price.

If both tickets are bought along with parking at a
total cost of £22.25, how much is the parking charge?   £_____

38. If pencils cost 59p each, and you get 56p change
from a £10 note, how many pencils have you bought? _____

/3

> Write all the **factors** for each of these numbers.

39. 24   →   _____, _____, _____, _____, _____, _____, _____, _____

40. 52   →   _____, _____, _____, _____, _____, _____

41. 81   →   _____, _____, _____, _____, _____

/3

> Look at the grid.

42.

What are the coordinates of rectangle A?

(☐,☐), (☐,☐), (☐,☐), (☐,☐)

43. Draw rectangle B at the following coordinates: (6, 4), (3, 4), (3, 9) and (6, 9).

44. Is rectangle B a **translation**, **rotation** or **reflection** of rectangle A? _____

/3

> Find these amounts.

45. $\frac{3}{8}$ of 64km _____

46. $\frac{3}{4}$ of 60mm _____

47. $\frac{2}{3}$ of 750ml _____

48. $\frac{3}{5}$ of 80kg _____

49. $\frac{4}{7}$ of 56m _____

50. $\frac{5}{6}$ of 78cm _____

/6

/50

PAPER 7

Write the next two numbers in these **sequences**.

1. 8.49   8.58   8.67   8.76   _____   _____

2. 12.078   12.079   12.08   12.081   _____   _____

3. 27.96   27.97   27.98   27.99   _____   _____   /3

Round these numbers to one decimal place.

4–9. 6.47 _____   8.92 _____   12.35 _____

15.03 _____   14.99 _____   9.05 _____   /6

Which of the numbers from the box belongs to each sequence?

352   315   216

10. 15   30   45   60   75   _____

11. 36   54   72   90   108   _____

12. 110   121   132   143   154   _____   /3

Answer these.

13–18. Write these decimals as fractions in their simplest form.

0.35 $\frac{\Box}{\Box}$ 0.6 $\frac{\Box}{\Box}$ 0.32 $\frac{\Box}{\Box}$

0.95 $\frac{\Box}{\Box}$ 0.98 $\frac{\Box}{\Box}$ 0.2 $\frac{\Box}{\Box}$ /6

19. Which three **prime numbers** multiply to make 255? $\Box \times \Box \times \Box = 255$ /1

Draw all the lines of **symmetry** on these shapes.

20–23.   /4

Parallelogram   Rectangle   Rhombus   Square   Trapezium   Kite

Calculate the missing angles. Do not use a **protractor**.

24–27.

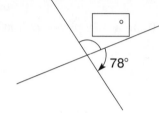

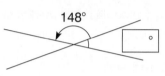

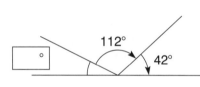

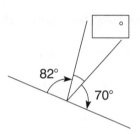

/4

Write the name of each of these shapes from its **net**.

28. _____   **29.** _____

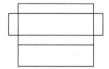

30. _____   /3

Level 5

Choose from the numbers 2, 3, 4, 7, 9 or 10 to complete these statements.

31. 300 is a **multiple** of ☐, ☐, ☐ and ☐.

32. 130 is a multiple of ☐ and ☐.

33. 150 is a multiple of ☐, ☐ and ☐.

34. 420 is a multiple of ☐, ☐, ☐, ☐ and ☐.

/4

Answer these.

35. The **ratio** of bananas to apples on a market stall is 4 : 9. There are 78 pieces of fruit altogether.

How many apples are there? _____

36. The **proportion** of red flowers in Percy's garden is $\frac{3}{8}$. There are 24 red flowers.

How many flowers are there in total in the garden? _____

37. Mr. Rich works $\frac{5}{7}$ of the way up a tall tower. He works on floor 60.

How many floors are there altogether? _____

/3

38. During the day the temperature was -6°C. During the night it fell another 7°C.

What was the temperature during the night? _____

/1

39. 20% of 250g _____

40. 25% of 440ml _____

41. 40% of £900 _____

42. 75% of 120kg _____

43. 70% of 120cm _____

44. 90% of 80p _____

/6

Insert brackets to make each number sentence correct.

45. 5 × 6 + 4 = 50

46. 36 ÷ 6 × 3 = 2

47. 3 + 6 × 2 = 18

48. 35 ÷ 5 + 2 = 5

49. 12 − 4 × 3 = 24

50. 24 + 12 ÷ 2 = 30

/6

/50

PAPER 8

Answer these.

1. 0.76 × 1000 = _____

2. 8457 ÷ 100 = _____

3. 46.3 ÷ 1000 = _____

4. 1.03 × 1000 = _____

5. 4.56 × 100 = _____

6. 589 ÷ 1000 = _____

 /6

Write each set of numbers in order, starting with the smallest.

7. -235   -253   -325   -523   -352   -532

   Smallest _____ _____ _____ _____ _____ _____ Biggest

8. 845   -234   854   -243   548   -342

   Smallest _____ _____ _____ _____ _____ _____ Biggest   /2

Work out **approximate** answers to these sums using the numbers in the box.

| 28 000   1500   15 000   4500   8000   6000 |

9. 223 × 20 _____

10. 405 × 15 _____

11. 42 × 36 _____

12. 672 × 12 _____

13. 940 × 30 _____

14. 306 × 51 _____

 /6

15. What is the smaller angle between the hands on the clock face? _____°

/1

16–17. Here are two sides of a parallelogram.

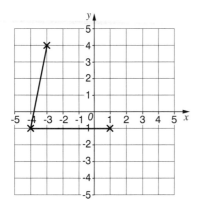

What are the **coordinates** of the fourth **vertex**? _____

Mark the missing coordinates for the fourth vertex and complete the parallelogram.   /2

18. Shade squares to make a **reflection** on the mirror line A–B.   /1

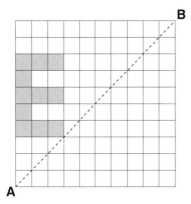

Work out these decimal sums.

19. 10.6 + 1.35 = _____   **20.** 12.29 + 0.06 = _____

21. 1.69 + 2.4 = _____   **22.** 13.07 + 2.64 = _____

23. 9.3 + 2.14 = _____   **24.** 9.56 + 8.78 = _____   /6

Join the pairs of prices to make £500.

25–27.

£189.12

£276.45

£223.55

£162.64

£310.88

£337.36

/3

Write the missing **digits** in these sums.

28–31. ▦ ▢26 × 12 = 271▢   ▢50 × 20 = 300▢   /4

Rearrange each set of digits to make the number nearest to 1000.

32. 8 4 9 1   ____ ____ ____ ____

33. 7 4 3 0   ____ ____ ____ ____   /2

You roll two dice. Work out these **probabilities**.

34. What is the **probability** of rolling two even numbers? _____

35. What is the probability of rolling one odd and one even number? _____

36. What is the probability of scoring a total greater than 1? _____   /3

These are the prices of some second-hand cars.
Work out the **mean**, **median** and **mode**.

37–39. ▦ (£935   £875   £799   £1995   £875   £1595   £895)

What is the mean price? _____

What is the median price? _____

What is the mode price? _____   /3

Solve these problems.

40. A tunnel is being built through a mountain. So far the workers have completed 11 miles
and the tunnel is 40% completed.

How long will the tunnel be when finished? _____   /1

41. Li is trying to raise money for charity and hopes to raise £1500. So far he has collected
60% of his target.

How much has he raised so far? _____   /1

42. ▦ A television costs £189 and a camera costs £167. In a sale the prices are
reduced by 15%.

If you buy both the television and the
camera in the sale, what will the total cost be? _____   /1

This scale measures in grams and ounces.

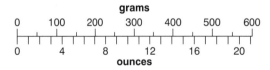

43. Approximately how many grams is 9 ounces to the nearest 50 grams? _____

44. Approximately how many ounces is 350 grams to the nearest ounce? _____   /2

Answer these.

45. The big triangle in the rectangle is an **isosceles triangle**. Work out the size of angle x without using a **protractor**.

$x =$ _____ °

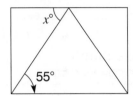

/1

46. I am thinking of a number. When I subtract 15 and multiply the number by 3 the answer is 15.

What number am I thinking of? _____

/1

47. A film starts at 20:15 and last 125 minutes.

What time does it finish? _____

/1

48. A concert starts at 19:35 and lasts 1 hour 56 minutes.

What time does it finish? _____

/1

Write pairs of **factors** for each number.

49. 48 → (1, _____) (_____ , _____) (_____ , _____)(_____ , _____)(_____ , _____)

50. 66 → (1, _____) (_____ , _____) (_____ , _____)(_____ , _____)

/2

/50

PAPER 9

Order these decimals from smallest to largest.

1. 1.356   1.36   1.306   1.4   1.35   1.45

Smallest _____ _____ _____ _____ _____ _____ Largest   /1

Work out the **approximate** amounts of money in these sums.

| £5000 | £2700 | £2000 | £6000 | £3000 | £1600 |

2. £53 × 40 _____   **3.** £75 × 42 _____   **4.** £99 × 51 _____

5. £120 × 50 _____   **6.** £91 × 30 _____   **7.** £79 × 22 _____   /6

Calculate these amounts.

8. 50% of 70cl _____   **9.** 35% of 200cl _____   **10.** 80% of 120cl _____

11. 65% of 50cl _____   **12.** 90% of 120cl _____   **13.** 35% of 80cl _____   /6

Answer these.

14. Order these fractions from smallest to largest.

$\frac{1}{2}$ $\frac{3}{8}$ $\frac{6}{9}$ $\frac{14}{25}$ $\frac{3}{5}$

Smallest _____ _____ _____ _____ _____ Largest   /1

15. Rotate the trapezium 90° **clockwise** around the point (1, 5).   /1

32

Decide which shapes are being described.

Parallelogram   **Rectangle**   **Rhombus**   **Square**   **Trapezium**   **Kite**

16. 1 set of **parallel** sides only. _____

17. 2 sets of parallel sides and all angles are 90°. _____ and _____

18. 2 sets of **adjacent** sides of the same length and only 1 set of equal angles. _____

19. 2 sets of parallel sides and 2 sets of equal angles. _____ and _____

20. All sides the same length and 2 sets of angles the same.

_____

/5

The pie chart shows the favourite sports of 120 children.

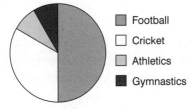

■ Football
□ Cricket
■ Athletics
■ Gymnastics

21. How many children prefer football?   _____

22. What fraction of the children prefer cricket?

23. How many children altogether prefer athletics and gymnastics?   _____   /3

Read these scales and write each weight in grams.

24.

_____

25.

_____ /2

Answer these.

26. A glass of orange juice and a glass of milkshake cost £2.35. Two glasses of orange juice and a glass of milkshake cost £3.60.

How much does a glass of milkshake cost? _____ /1

27. One adult and one child go to the cinema at a cost of £15.85. Two adults and one child go to the cinema at a cost of £25.35.

How much does a child's ticket cost? _____ /1

28. Mr. Monty's lawn is 12 metres long and 8 metres wide. He wants to know how many daisies are in his lawn. He decides to **estimate** how many daisies are in the lawn by counting the ones in a small **area** and estimating. He counts 36 daisies in an area 1m long and $\frac{1}{2}$ metre wide.

▦ Estimate how many daisies in the whole lawn. _____ /1

29. Draw the **reflection** of the kite along the mirror line A–B. /1

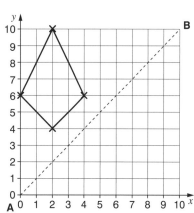

30. 980 ÷ 20 = _____

31. 720 ÷ 15 = _____

32. 510 ÷ 17 = _____ /3

Write down the missing numbers in these **sequences**.

33. _____   _____   _____   16   25   36   49   _____   _____   _____

34. 2   3   5   7   11   13   17   _____   _____   _____

35. _____   _____   _____   11   23   35   _____   _____   _____   /3

Answer these.

36–40. Using the **equation** $y = x + 3$ plot a line graph with the following values of x:

-5   -3   0   4   /5

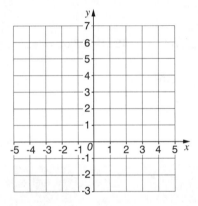

41–43. In a year group, 82 children were asked which of two languages they preferred. The results are shown in the table below.

	French	German
Boys	23	
Girls	25	20

Complete the table.

How many more children prefer French to German? _____

How many more girls were asked than boys? _____   /3

Calculate the shaded area of these shapes.

44.

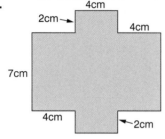

4cm
2cm
4cm
8cm
7cm
4cm
2cm

45.

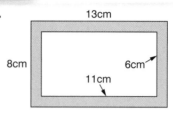

13cm
6cm
11cm

_____   _____   /2

Answer these.

46. 0.3 metres = _____mm   **47.** 1.01 litres = _____ml   **48.** 0.003kg = _____g

49. 0.03 litres = _____ml   **50.** 0.56km = _____ metres   /5

/50

PAPER 10

Round these numbers to two decimal places.

1. 5.566 _____   **2.** -3.861 _____   **3.** 6.239 _____

4. -0.025 _____   **5.** 4.205 _____   **6.** -3.117 _____   /6

Write these fractions in their simplest form.

7. $\dfrac{9}{45} = \dfrac{\square}{\square}$ **8.** $\dfrac{36}{84} = \dfrac{\square}{\square}$ **9.** $\dfrac{20}{48} = \dfrac{\square}{\square}$

10. $\dfrac{49}{56} = \dfrac{\square}{\square}$ **11.** $\dfrac{18}{72} = \dfrac{\square}{\square}$ **12.** $\dfrac{16}{56} = \dfrac{\square}{\square}$ /6

Answer booklet: More Maths age 10–11

Paper 1

1. c) £180

2–7.

×	3	8	6
3	9	24	18
4	12	32	24
7	21	56	42

8–9. 23, 29

10. b) 7

11. 67 300

12. 35 700

13. 39 700

14. $\frac{3}{8}, \frac{4}{10}, \frac{2}{3}, \frac{5}{6}$

15. 350cm

16. 625cm

17. 875cm

18. 1250cm

19. 25cm

20. 2075cm

21. 35°

22. 140°

23. 90°

24. 10:50

25. 17:10

26. 09:15

27. 20:43

28. 69 miles

29. £390

30. 84 stairs

31. 148 metres

32. $\frac{2}{5}$

33. 7759

34. 3273

35. 7874

36. 1391

37. D

38. C

39. A

40. B

41. 62

42. 61

43. 206

44. 67

45. 6

46. 4

47. 6

48. 1100ml = 1.1 litres

49. 400ml = 0.4 litres

50. 1900ml = 1.9 litres

Paper 2

1. $\frac{7}{10}$

2. $\frac{3}{10}$

3. $\frac{9}{100}$

4. $\frac{67}{100}$

5. 6445, 6455, 6465

6. 8766, 8756, 8746

7. 9049, 9149, 9249

8. 4116, 4016, 3916

9. £287.30

10. £22.46

11. £31.70

12–15.

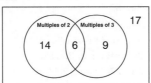

16. $8 \times 7 > 9 \times 6$

17. $12 \times 3 = 9 \times 4$

18. $84 \div 12 < 64 \div 8$

19. $121 \div 11 = 132 \div 12$

20. 17

21. $\frac{2}{3}$

22. $\frac{1}{3}$

23. 0

24. 1

25. 801, 804, 807

26. 351, 344, 337

27. 5, 11, 17

28. -21, -31, -41

29. 1h 45min

30–33.

IN	6	9	12	8
OUT	39	54	69	49

34.
```
  5729
  3468
  ----
  2261
```

35.
```
  8218
  6249
  ----
  1969
```

49. 400ml = 0.4 litres

50. 1900ml = 1.9 litres

36–39.

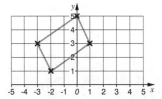

40. (-3, 3)

41–42. Area = 88m²
Perimeter = 48m

43. 11.99

44. £245

45. 39, 56

46. 39, 21

47. 56

48. 83, 47

49. 56

50. 39, 47 and 83

Paper 3

1. 24, 48

2.

3. 45g, 78g, 780g, 4.5kg, 7800g, 7.9kg, 78kg

4–5.

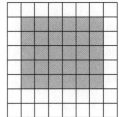

Any rectangle measuring
5 squares by 6 squares

6. 1.363

7. 100

8. 200.1

9. 100

10. $\frac{2}{3}$

11. $\frac{4}{5}$

12. $\frac{4}{9}$

13. $\frac{1}{4}$

14. 18
15. 8
16–21.

+	76	43	62
32	108	75	94
56	132	99	118
83	159	126	145

22. $27 \div (12 - 3) = 3$
23. $(6 \times 5) \div 3 = 10$
24. $36 \div (2 + 4) = 6$
25. $(8 \times 6) + 2 = 50$
26. $4 + (4 \times 5) = 24$
27. $(12 - 8) \div 2 = 2$
28. 9
29. 20
30. £64
31. 10
32. 24
33. 600g = 0.6kg
34. 1200g = 1.2kg
35. 1700g = 1.7kg
36. Lilly
37. 20 metres
38. Mike
39. Lilly, Tom, Mike, Sara, Harry
40. 63
41. 15
42. 168
43. 45
44. 45
45. 126
46. 130
47. $\frac{1}{12}$, 8.3% or 0.08
48. $\frac{1}{4}$, 25% or 0.25
49. $\frac{1}{3}$, 33.3% or 0.33
50. $\frac{7}{24}$, 29.2% or 0.29

Paper 4
1. 0, -19
2. -15, -29
3. 40, 63
4. -39, -55
5. 16.6
6. 21.9
7. 14.2
8. 10.2
9. 26.6

10. 16.8
11. -19°C, -14°C, -11°C, -3°C, -1°C
12–13. 29, 37
14. 0.4
15. 0.75
16. 0.3
17. 0.56
18. 0.32
19. 0.32
20. 5.3
21. 8.9
22. 9.4
23. 75.3
24. 27.4
25. 91.5
26. 155
27. 8
28. 6
29. 3
30. (-5, -4), (-5, 1), (4, 1), (4, -4)
31. 137°
32. 83°
33. 2540g or 2.54kg
34. 1825ml or 1.825 litres
35. 3475m or 3.475km
36. 2707g or 2.707kg
37. 5525ml or 5.525 litres
38. 4102m or 4.102km
39. 10°C
40. Area = 48cm²
41. Perimeter = 32cm
42. Area = 138cm²
43. Perimeter = 58cm
44. 28805
45. 6266
46. 14712
47. 8800
48. 47
49. 54
50. 72

Paper 5
1. 120ml
2. 4kg
3. 48cm
4. 42m
5. 142.5mm
6. 6km
7. £8.60
8. £9.30
9. £11.50
10. £11.00
11. £13.00

12. £14.40
13. 19, 23
14. 27°
15. 32°
16. 1m
17. 4m
18. 300ml
19. 5kg
20. 10 litres
21. 70kg
22. 32km
23. 46
24. 10
25. 18
26. 13cm
27. 24cm
28. 20cm²
29. 20 goals
30. 124
31. 261 miles
32–39.

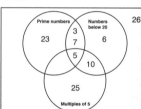

40–45.

	Music	Art	Total
Boys	49	53	102
Girls	48	46	94
Total	97	99	196

46. $20\% < \frac{1}{4}$
47. $0.5 = \frac{1}{2}$
48. $35\% > \frac{3}{10}$
49. $\frac{1}{9} > 9\%$
50. $0.6 = \frac{3}{5}$

Paper 6
1. 100
2. 10
3. 4960
4. 100
5. 526.9
6. 100
7. 1hr 15min
8. 3hr 25min
9. 4hr 55min

10. 47 min
11. 6cm²
12. 17.5cm²
13. 25cm²
14. 50%
15. 90%
16. 72%
17. 60%
18. 25%
19. 70%
20. 1
21. -1
22. 11
23. 30 miles
24. 10
25. 81
26. 12
27. 6 and 8
28. (0, 2)
29. 200°
30. 70°
31. 8
32. 142.68
33. 116.15
34. 171.09
35. 17cm
36. £3.70
37. £5.00
38. 16
39. 1, 2, 3, 4, 6, 8, 12, 24
40. 1, 2, 4, 13, 26, 52
41. 1, 3, 9, 27, 81
42. (1, 1), (6, 1), (1, 4), (6, 4)
43.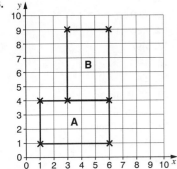
44. Rotation
45. 24km
46. 45mm
47. 500ml
48. 48kg
49. 32m
50. 65cm

Paper 7
1. 8.85, 8.94
2. 12.082, 12.083
3. 28, 28.01
4. 6.5
5. 8.9
6. 12.4
7. 15.0
8. 15.0
9. 9.1
10. 315
11. 216
12. 352
13. $\frac{7}{20}$
14. $\frac{3}{5}$
15. $\frac{8}{25}$
16. $\frac{19}{20}$
17. $\frac{49}{50}$
18. $\frac{1}{5}$
19. 3, 5, 17
20–23.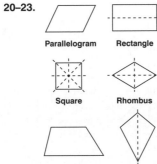

Parallelogram   Rectangle

Square   Rhombus

Trapezium   Kite

24. 102°
25. 32°
26. 26°
27. 28°
28. Octahedron
29. Triangular-based pyramid or tetrahedron
30. Cuboid
31. 2, 3, 4, 10
32. 2, 10
33. 2, 3, 10
34. 2, 3, 4, 7, 10
35. 54
36. 64
37. 84
38. -13°C
39. 50g

40. 110ml
41. £360
42. 90kg
43. 84cm
44. 72p
45. 5 × (6 + 4) = 50
46. 36 ÷ (6 × 3) = 2
47. (3 + 6) × 2 = 18
48. 35 ÷ (5 + 2) = 5
49. (12 – 4) × 3 = 24
50. 24 + (12 ÷ 2) = 30

Paper 8
1. 760
2. 84.57
3. 0.0463
4. 1030
5. 456
6. 0.589
7. -532, -523, -352, -325, -253, -235
8. -342, -243, -234, 548, 845, 854
9. 4500
10. 6000
11. 1500
12. 8000
13. 28 000
14. 15 000
15. 120°
16. (2, 4)
17.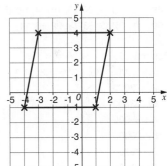

18.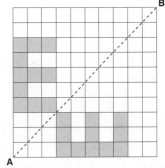

19. 11.95
20. 12.35
21. 4.09
22. 15.71
23. 11.44
24. 18.34
25. £189.12 + £310.88
26. £223.55 + £276.45
27. £162.64 + £337.36
28–29. 226 × 12 = 2712
30–31. 150 × 20 = 3000
32. 1489
33. 0743
34. $\frac{1}{4}$ or 0.25 or 25%
35. $\frac{1}{2}$ or 0.5 or 50%
36. 1 or 100%
37. £1138.43
38. £895
39. £875
40. 27.5 miles
41. £900
42. £302.60
43. 250g
44. 12 ounces
45. 55°
46. 20
47. 22:20 or 10.20pm
48. 21:31 or 9.31pm
49. (1, 48) (2, 24) (3, 16) (4, 12) (6, 8)
50. (1, 66) (2, 33) (3, 22) (6, 11)

Paper 9
1. 1.306, 1.35, 1.356, 1.36, 1.4, 1.45
2. £2000
3. £3000
4. £5000
5. £6000
6. £2700
7. £1600
8. 35cl
9. 70cl
10. 96cl
11. 32.5cl
12. 108cl
13. 28cl
14. $\frac{3}{8}, \frac{1}{2}, \frac{14}{25}, \frac{3}{5}, \frac{6}{9}$

15.

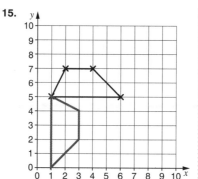

16. Trapezium
17. Square and rectangle
18. Kite
19. Parallelogram and rhombus
20. Rhombus
21. 60
22. $\frac{1}{3}$
23. 20
24. 6.5–7g
25. 85–90g
26. £1.10
27. £6.35
28. 6912
29.

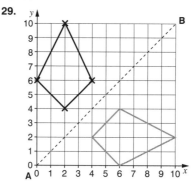

30. 49
31. 48
32. 30
33. 1, 4, 9, 16, 25, 36, 49, 64, 81, 100
34. 2, 3, 5, 7, 11, 13, 17, 19, 23, 29
35. -25, -13, -1, 11, 23, 35, 47, 59, 71
36–40.

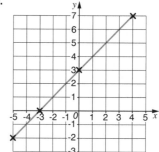

41.

	French	German
Boys	23	14
Girls	25	20

42. 14
43. 8
44. 100cm²
45. 38cm²
46. 300mm
47. 1010ml
48. 3g
49. 30ml
50. 560 metres

Paper 10
1. 5.57
2. -3.86
3. 6.24
4. -0.03
5. 4.21
6. -3.12
7. $\frac{1}{5}$
8. $\frac{3}{7}$
9. $\frac{5}{12}$
10. $\frac{7}{8}$
11. $\frac{1}{4}$
12. $\frac{2}{7}$
13. 49, 81
14. 270
15. 329
16. 195
17. 49
18. 68
19. 54
20. 25.8 miles
21. 2.09pm
22. 3 fizzy drinks
2 cups of coffee
23. $x + 5$
24. $y - 6$
25. $2n - 3$
26. $\frac{p}{2} + 4$
27. $\frac{1}{3}$, 33.3% or 0.33
28. $\frac{5}{6}$, 83.3% or 0.83
29. $\frac{1}{2}$, 50% or 0.5

30. (2, 5)

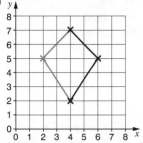

31. -4

32. -12

33. 5

34. -26

35. -17

36. 4

37. =

38. >

39. <

40. =

41. $\frac{4}{10}, \frac{6}{16}, \frac{11}{30}, \frac{13}{40}, \frac{8}{25}, \frac{6}{20}$

42. $a = 1$

43. $a = -4$

44. $a = 5$

45. $a = 4$

46. 24

47. True

48. False

49. True

50. False

Paper 11

1. 6.88 metres

2. 4.26 litres

3. 8.01 kg

4. 7.10 litres

5. 5.04 kg

6. 4.00 metres

7. 0.8

8. 0.7

9. 0.3

10. 0.45

11. $\frac{3}{4}$

12. $\frac{9}{20}$

13. $\frac{6}{25}$

14. $\frac{13}{20}$

15. 12

16. 81

17. 54

18. 36

19. $\frac{1}{3}$

20. $\frac{2}{5}$

21. $\frac{9}{10}$

22. 12

23. 2100

24. 864

25. 56m²

26. 40%

27. 70%

28. 80%

29. 25%

30. Big Ben

31. 60

32. 10

33.

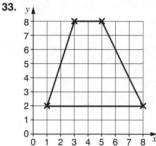

34. Trapezium

35. 0.305   0.35   0.355   0.5
0.505   0.535

36. Poor chance

37. Certain

38. Impossible

39. Good chance

40. 8.85   8.94

41. 11.01   11.03

42. 0.98   0.96

43. 45°

44. £112

45. 104

46. Reflected

47. 4

48. 2

49. 7

50. 3

Paper 12

1. 0.45, $\frac{2}{5}$, $\frac{3}{8}$, 0.35, $\frac{1}{3}$, $\frac{1}{4}$

2. 147 and 196

3. 235 and 451

4. 147 and 201

5. 196

6. 451, 201 and 196

7. 196

8–13.

×	600	300	500
80	48 000	24 000	40 000
20	12 000	6000	10 000
50	30 000	15 000	25 000

14. $a = 68°$

15. $b = 83°$

16. £68

17. £95.20

18. Bicycle, laptop, violin

19. £32

20. 9.95

21. 1, 3, 9

22. 99

23. 8

24. 600 metres

25. 1 minute

26. $4\frac{1}{2}$ minutes

27. 1400 metres

28. 9100

29. 6600

30. Box B

31. 8cm³

32. 6h 45min

33. Train 3

34. Train 2

35. Train 2

36. 2h 50min

37. 5h 10min

38. 900g

39. 28 ounces

40. 258

41. 35%

42. $\frac{3}{5}$

43. $\frac{9}{10}$

44. 9.367 < 9.376 < 9.673 < 9.763

45. 11.342 > 11.32 > 11.3 > 11.243

46–50.

IN	366	186	506	216	796
OUT	19	10	26	11.5	40.5

Paper 13

1. -9.457

2. -4.861

3. -2.500

4. -7.770

5. -1.000

6. -3.101

7. -8.96 -8.69 -8.31 -8.19
-8.09 -8.06 -8.01

8. 1009.7 1009.9 1011.7
1011.9 1012.9 1013 1013.2

9. 112.863 112.864 112.865
112.867 112.869 112.872

10. -0.36 -0.365 -0.368 -0.37
-0.373 -0.377

11. 30

12. Perfume B (70ml)

13. $\frac{3}{8}$, $\frac{4}{10}$, $\frac{2}{3}$, $\frac{5}{6}$

14. 39.34

15. 18

16. 50%

17. 13

18. 5

19–27.

÷	288 sweets	576 sweets	864 sweets
24 children	12	24	36
32 children	9	18	27
36 children	8	16	24

28. 8cm × 8cm × 8cm

29. 4cm

30. 89 and 97

31.

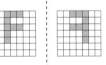

32. 1, 2 and 4

33. 1, 2, 3 and 6

34. 1, 2 and 4

35. 1, 2, 4, 5, 8, 10, 20 and 40

36. 600

37. 100

38. 2

39–40.

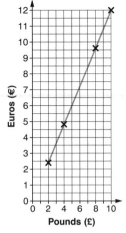

41. 1.20 euros

42. 11.4 euros

43. £4.17

44. £8.33

45. 600 euros

46. £416.67

47. 0.449

48. 12.635 and 12.684

49. 12.235

50. 12.569

Paper 14

1. 27.65

2. 0.8731

3. 28

4. 36

5. 12

6. 18

7. 4h 11min

8. 5h 2min

9. 5h 46min

10. 3h 38min

11. 19

12. 45

13.   4652
     -1893
     2759

14.   8324
     -3556
     4768

15.   2300
     -1459
     841

16.   7351
     -6248
     1103

17. 85

18. £7650

19. Car B

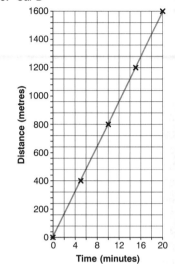

20. 480 metres

21. 960 metres

22. $2\frac{1}{2}$ minutes or
2 minutes 30 seconds

23. $16\frac{1}{4}$ minutes or 16 minutes
16 minutes 15 seconds

24. 15

25. 66

26. 39m

27. $(45 - 15) + 18 = 48$

28. $10 \times (6 + 2) = 80$

29. $(5 + 50) \div 5 = 11$

30. $(28 - 14) \times 2 = 28$

31. $36 \div (6 + 3) = 4$

32. 26.49

33. 89.83

34. 200.05

35. Perimeter = 26cm   Area = 16cm²

36. Perimeter = 28m   Area = 39m²

37. <

38. >

39. >

40. <

41. <

42. >

43. $\frac{1}{3}$

44. $\frac{1}{4}$

45. 1

46. 0

47. Children's

48. Family

49. 24
50. 107

aper 15
1. 91196, 90196, 89196
2. 30300, 31300, 32300
3. 81023, 71023, 61023
4. 72956, 82956, 92956
5. 100km
6. 80km
7. 210km
8. 170km
9. 292
10. 101
11. 2
12. 1560
13. £124
14. 135 pages
15. 375m
16. 415kg
17. 4
18. 2
19. 2
20. 1
21. 1
2–30.

	Round to the nearest 100	Round to the nearest 1000	Round to the nearest 10000
7632	7600	8000	10000
86523	86500	87000	90000
31989	32000	32000	30000

31. $x = 32°$
32. $2x = 64°$
33. $x = 22°$
34. $2x = 44°$
35. 24767
36. 19481
37. 7769
38. 9764
39. 13
40. 16
41. 20
42. February, June, October
43. March, November
44. 6
45. 141
46. $\frac{1}{2}$, 50% or 0.5
47. $\frac{3}{10}$, 33% or 0.33

48. $\frac{1}{5}$, 20% or 0.2
49. $\frac{1}{10}$, 10% or 0.1
50. $\frac{2}{5}$, 40% or 0.4

Paper 16
1. 2.8
2. 20
3. 3.7
4. 20
5. 6448
6. 200
7. 8
8. 1
9. 12
10. -2
11. 15
12. 10.56 litres
13. 3
14. 1
15. 1
16–21.

	Pizza	Fish and chips	Total
Adults	24	78	102
Children	69	42	111
Total	93	120	213

22. (16, 15)
23. (24, 18)
24. 75 miles
25. 37.5 miles
26. 68.75 miles
27. 31.25 miles
28. 16
29. 2100 miles
30. 7420 miles
31. 66.6%
32. 3600 miles
33. £1400
34. Day 4
35. Days 4 and 5
36. 120
37. 50
38. 10
39. 9
40. 400g
41. 150 metres
42. 5ml
43. 40km
44. 1kg

45. 2 litres
46. 5 1425 ÷ 25 = 57
47. 5
48. 83968 ÷ 32 = 124
49. 4
50. 5

Paper 17
1. 16, 81, 121
2–10.

	Round to the nearest 100	Round to the nearest 1000	Round to the nearest 10000
Brigfield 34293	34300	34000	30000
Nottibury 49584	49600	50000	50000
Liverton 69017	69000	69000	70000

11. $a = 65°$
12. $b = 115°$
13. $c = 80°$
14. $d = 100°$
15. £318.42 + £181.58
16. £381.24 + £118.76
17. £388.42 + £111.58
18. 649m
19. Lhotse 1
20. Kanchenjunga
21. 26048m
22. 442.5m
23. 8856m
24. 10
25. 2
26. 245
27. 504
28. 448
29. $\frac{1}{2}$
30. $\frac{1}{5}$
31. $\frac{4}{5}$
32. $\frac{1}{10}$
33. $\frac{3}{20}$
34. 9.85
35. 9.85
36. 9.9
37. 420cm or 4.2 metres

38. 6.5   13   26   52   104   208   416

39. $3\frac{1}{3}$ 10   30   90   270

   810   2430

40. 1   4   16   64   256   1024   4096

41. (3, 4) (1, 7) (3, 9) (5, 7)

42.

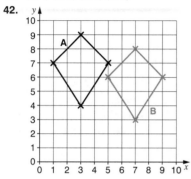

43. Translation

44. False

45. False

46. True

47. True

48. True

49. 49m²

50. 14m

Answer these.

13. What two **square numbers** below 100 when multiplied together make 3969?

_____ × _____ = 3969   /1

14. 45 × 6 = _____   **15.** 47 × 7 = _____   **16.** 39 × 5 = _____

17. 13$\overline{637}$ = _____   **18.** 12$\overline{816}$ = _____   **19.** 14$\overline{756}$ = _____   /6

Work these out.

20. The first day Abigail cycles 12 miles on her bike. The second day she cycles 15% further than the first day.

How far has she cycled in total during the two days? _____   /1

21. It takes 2 hours 35 minutes for a train to complete its journey.

If it leaves at 11.34am, what time does it arrive? _____   /1

22. At the cafe, a fizzy drink costs £1.09 and a cup of coffee costs £1.45. A family spends a total of £6.17. They buy 1 more fizzy drink than cups of coffee.

How many of each do they buy?   _____ fizzy drinks   _____ cups of coffee   /1

Write simple **expressions** for these.

23. 5 more than x = _____   **24.** 6 less than y = _____

25. 3 less than 2 lots of n = _____   **26.** 4 more than $\frac{1}{2}$ of p = _____   /4

Answer these as a fraction.

27–29. In a bag of different coloured balls, there are 12 red, 10 green, 8 yellow and 6 blue ones.

What is the chance of choosing a red ball? _____

What is the chance of not choosing a blue one? _____

What is the chance of choosing a green or yellow ball? _____   /3

Here are two sides of a shape.

30. Plot the fourth **coordinate** to make a kite and complete the shape.

/1

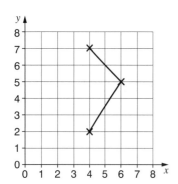

Work these out.

31. -8 − -4 = _____

32. -5 + -7 = _____

33. 12 + -7 = _____

34. -14 + -12 = _____

35. -11 − 6 = _____

36. 1 − -3 = _____

/6

Write <, > or = between each pairs of amounts.

37. $\frac{2}{3}$ of 90 ☐ $\frac{3}{4}$ of 80

38. $\frac{4}{5}$ of 35 ☐ $\frac{3}{4}$ of 36

39. $\frac{7}{8}$ of 64 ☐ $\frac{6}{8}$ of 80

40. $\frac{2}{7}$ of 42 ☐ $\frac{4}{5}$ of 15

/4

Order these fractions from largest to smallest.

41. $\frac{13}{40}$ $\frac{11}{30}$ $\frac{6}{20}$ $\frac{6}{16}$ $\frac{4}{10}$ $\frac{8}{25}$

_____   _____   _____   _____   _____   _____

/1

Find the value of *a* in these expressions.

42. $6a − 11 = -5$

43. $23 = -9 − 8a$

$a =$ _____

$a =$ _____

44. $16 - 3a = 1$

45. $27 = 10a - 13$

$a =$ _____

$a =$ _____

/4

46. To celebrate his birthday Alan buys flapjacks and currant buns in the **ratio** 3:1.

If he bought a mix of 32 flapjacks and currant buns, how many flapjacks did he buy?

_____

/1

Tick true or false for each of these statements.

47. Circles have an **infinite** number of lines of **symmetry**.　　True ☐　　False ☐

48. Kites have two lines of symmetry.　　True ☐　　False ☐

49. An equilateral triangle has three lines of symmetry.　　True ☐　　False ☐

50. A rectangle has four lines of symmetry.　　True ☐　　False ☐

/4

/50

PAPER 11

Round these amounts to two decimal places.

1. 6.876 metres _____

2. 4.255 litres _____

3. 8.006kg _____

4. 7.096 litres _____

5. 5.044kg _____

6. 3.995 metres _____

/6

Change these fractions to decimals.

7. $\frac{4}{5} =$ _____

8. $\frac{7}{10} =$ _____

9. $\frac{6}{20} =$ _____

10. $\frac{9}{20} =$ _____

/4

Change these decimals to fractions in their simplest form.

11. $0.75 = \dfrac{\Box}{\Box}$

12. $0.45 = \dfrac{\Box}{\Box}$

13. $0.24 = \dfrac{\Box}{\Box}$

14. $0.65 = \dfrac{\Box}{\Box}$

/4

Answer these.

15. What is $\sqrt{144}$? _____

16. What is the next **square number** after 64? _____

17. $7^2 + \sqrt{25} =$ _____

18. $3^2 \times 2^2 =$ _____

/4

19–21. What fraction of 30 metres is:

10 metres $\dfrac{\Box}{\Box}$ 12 metres $\dfrac{\Box}{\Box}$ 27 metres $\dfrac{\Box}{\Box}$

/3

Circle the best **estimate**.

22. $145.75 \div 12.12 =$

8   9   10   11   12   13   14

23. $70.89 \times 29.36 =$

2000   2100   2300   2500   2900

/2

Answer these.

24. In the library the **proportion** of children's to adults' books is $3:8$.

If there are 324 children's books in the
library, how many adults' books are there? _____

/1

25. Jamie's lawn is 72m². He has mowed $\dfrac{7}{9}$ of it.

How much of his lawn has he mowed? _____m²

/1

Express the sale price as a **percentage** of the normal price.

26. | $\dfrac{3}{5}$ **off** |
Sale price

_____

27. | $\dfrac{15}{50}$ **off all prices** |
Sale price

_____

28. | $\frac{2}{10}$ discount | Sale price

_____

29. | $\frac{3}{4}$ off everything | Sale price

_____

/4

Look at the pie charts.

The pie charts show the favourite attractions of two different class visits to London.
In May, 120 children visited and in June, 160 children visited.

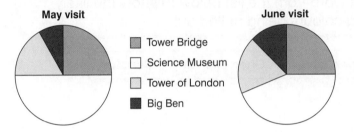

May visit   June visit

■ Tower Bridge
□ Science Museum
□ Tower of London
■ Big Ben

30. Which attraction was least popular on both visits? _____

31. How many children preferred the Science Museum in May? _____

32. How many more children liked Tower Bridge in June compared to May? _____

/3

Follow the instructions to complete the graph.

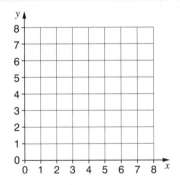

33. Plot these points on the graph and join them up: (1, 2), (8, 2), (5, 8) and (3, 8).

34. What shape have you drawn? _____

/2

Order these decimals starting with the smallest.

35. 0.5   0.35   0.305   0.355   0.505   0.535

_____   _____   _____   _____   _____   _____   /1

All the balls on a snooker table are put into a bag. There are 15 reds, then 1 each of the following: yellow, green, brown, blue, pink, black and the white. Choose a word from the list below to show the likely outcome of the following colours being pulled out.

Impossible   Poor chance   Good chance   Certain

36. A black is _____

37. A ball of any colour is _____

38. A grey ball is _____

39. A red is _____   /4

Continue these patterns for two more numbers.

40. 8.49   8.58   8.67   8.76   _____   _____

41. 10.93   10.95   10.97   10.99   _____   _____

42. 1.06   1.04   1.02   1.00   _____   _____   /3

Answer these.

43. What is the size of the angle marked x? _____°   /1

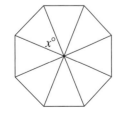

44. Your school is holding a disco for charity. 140 children turn up and pay the 50p entry fee. $\frac{3}{4}$ of them also pay 40p for a bag of sweets.

 How much money did your school make for charity at the disco? £ _____   /1

45. Tom has decided to give away some of his 240 CDs. He gives 40% away to one friend and $\frac{1}{6}$ to another.

How many CDs does he keep? _____   /1

46.

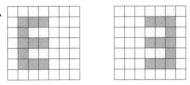

Has this shape been **translated**, **rotated** or **reflected**? _____   /1

Look at these results of football matches from two Saturdays and then answer the questions.

First Saturday	2–3	2–1	4–0	0–1	3–2
Second Saturday	3–0	7–2	1–2	3–3	0–1

47. What was the **range** of goals scored on the first Saturday? _____

48. Looking at the goals scored on the first Saturday, what is the **mode** number of goals?

_____

49. What is the range of results for the second Saturday? _____

50. Looking at the goals scored on the second Saturday, what is the mode number of goals?

_____   /4

/50

PAPER 12

Order these numbers starting with the largest.

1. $\frac{1}{4}$ 0.45 $\frac{2}{5}$ $\frac{3}{8}$ 0.35 $\frac{1}{3}$

_____   _____   _____   _____   _____   _____

/1

Choose from these numbers to answer each question.

147   235   451   201   196

2. Which two numbers can be divided exactly by 7? _____ and _____

3. Which two numbers leave a **remainder** of 1 when divided by 9? _____ and _____

4. Which two numbers can be divided exactly by 3? _____ and _____

5. Which number leaves a remainder of 4 when divided by 8? _____

6. Which three numbers leave a remainder of 1 when divided by 5? _____, _____ and _____

7. Which number can be divided exactly by 4? _____

/6

Complete this multiplication table.

8–13.

/6

×	_____	300	500
80	48 000	24 000	40 000
20		6000	
_____			25 000

Find the missing angles.

14.

15.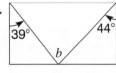

Angle *a* = _____

Angle *b* = _____

/2

All these items are put in the sale and will have 20% off the normal price.

| **Bicycle** £85 | **Laptop** £99 | **Scooter** £34 | **Violin** £59 |

16. What is the new price of the bicycle? _____

17. What price can the bicycle and scooter be bought for now? _____

18. Which three items can be now be bought for just under £195?

_____

19. What is the new **difference** in price between a laptop and violin? _____

/4

Answer these.

20. Which number, when rounded to one decimal place, equals 10? Circle the correct answer.

9.12   10.1   9.95   10.09   10.99

/1

21. Circle the three **factors** which 36 and 45 share.

1   2   3   4   5   6   9   12   15   18

/1

22. Suzanna does 36 skips in a minute.

At the same rate, how many skips can she do in 2 minutes 45 seconds? _____

/1

23. I'm thinking of a number. If I triple it and then add 6, the answer is 30.

What number am I thinking of? _____

/1

Kelly is running on a running track at a steady speed. The table shows how far she has gone at different times. Plot these figures on the graph and answer the questions.

Time (minutes)	2	4	6	8
Distance (metres)	400	800	1200	1600

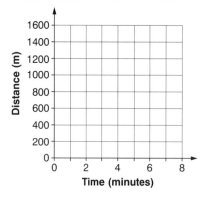

24. How far has Kelly run after 3 minutes? _____

25. How long does it take Kelly to run 200 metres? _____

26. How long does it take her to run 900 metres? _____

27. How far has she run in 7 minutes? _____

/4

Work out these sums.

28. 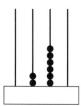 × 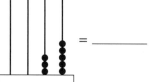 = _____

29. × 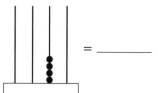 = _____

/2

Look at the boxes.

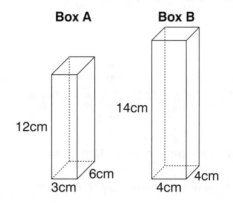

Box A   Box B

14cm

12cm

6cm

3cm

4cm

4cm

30. Which box has the greatest **volume**? _____

31. What is the difference in volume between the Box A and Box B? _____

/2

The timetable shows the times of three trains that run from Old Town to Barbury via two other stations.

	Train 1	Train 2	Train 3
Old Town	07:50	09:30	13:00
Newburton	08:30	10:20	13:40
Blackhill	11:10	13:30	16:25
Barbury	14:35	17:45	19:45

32. How long does the first train of the day take to travel from Old Town to Barbury? _____

33. Which train takes 3 hours 20 minutes to travel from Blackhill to Barbury? _____

34. Which train does the whole journey in the slowest time? _____

35. Which is the best train if you are meeting a friend at Barbury at 7.30 in the evening? _____

36. If you arrived at Blackhill at 13:35, how long would you have to wait for the next train? _____

37. If you travelled to Barbury on the first train and another friend is travelling on the last train, how long before your friend arrives? _____

/6

This scale measures in grams and ounces.

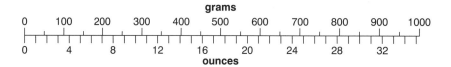

38. Approximately how many grams is 32 ounces? _____

39. Approximately how many ounces is 800 grams? _____ /2

Ari is reading a book of 860 pages. Answer these questions.

40. He is 30% of his way through the book. How many pages has he read? _____

41. He reads a further 43 pages. What **percentage** of the book has he now read? _____

42. When he gets to page number 516, what fraction of the book has he read? _____

43. When he has read 774 pages, what fraction of the book has he read? _____ /4

Write each set of decimals in order in the boxes to make these correct.

44. 9.673   9.763   9.367   9.376

☐ < ☐ < ☐ < ☐ /1

45. 11.243   11.342   11.32   11.3

☐ > ☐ > ☐ > ☐ /1

This function machine adds 14 and then divides numbers by 20.

46–50. Complete the table of results for the numbers coming out of the function machine.

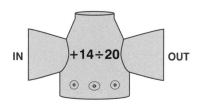

IN → +14÷20 → OUT

IN	366	186	506	216	796
OUT					

/5

/50

PAPER 13

Round these numbers to three decimal places.

1. -9.4565 _____   **2.** -4.8613 _____   **3.** -2.4995 _____

4. -7.7695 _____   **5.** -0.9996 _____   **6.** -3.1009 _____   /6

Two numbers in each of these groups of numbers are in the wrong place. Move the numbers so that all the numbers are in size order. The first number should stay in the same place each time.

7. -8.96   -8.69   -8.31   -8.01   -8.09   -8.06   -8.19

_____ _____ _____ _____ _____ _____ _____

8. 1009.7   1009.9   1011.7   1012.9   1011.9   1013   1013.2

_____ _____ _____ _____ _____ _____ _____

9. 112.863   112.867   112.865   112.864   112.869   112.872

_____ _____ _____ _____ _____ _____

10. -0.36   -0.368   -0.365   -0.37   -0.373   -0.377

_____ _____ _____ _____ _____ _____   /4

Answer these.

11. A footballer plays in 36 games during the season. He scores 3 goals in 2 of the games, 2 goals in a $\frac{1}{4}$ of the games and 1 goal in a $\frac{1}{6}$ of the games.

How many goals does he score in the season? _____   /1

12. At the local chemist, perfume sells in these size bottles at these prices.

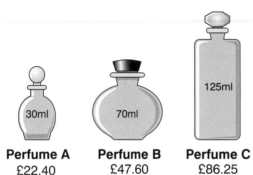

Perfume A **Perfume B** **Perfume C**
£22.40   £47.60   £86.25

Which perfume is best value for money? _____   /1

13. Put these fractions in order smallest to largest.

$\frac{4}{10}$ $\frac{3}{8}$ $\frac{5}{6}$ $\frac{2}{3}$

Smallest _____   _____   _____   _____ Largest   /1

14. Which number when rounded to one decimal place equals 39.3? Circle the correct number.

39.24   39.35   39.34   39.355   39.2   /1

Look at the pie charts. They show the favourite sports of 36 boys and 32 girls in Year 6. Answer the questions.

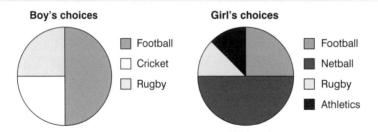

15. How many boys liked football? _____

16. What **percentage** of girls liked netball? _____%

17. How many children liked rugby? _____

18. How many more boys liked rugby than girls? _____   /4

Complete this division chart showing the number of sweets shared between children in different sized classes.

19–27.

÷	288 sweets	576 sweets	864 sweets
24 children			
32 children			
36 children			

/9

Answer these.

28. What are the dimensions of a cube with a **volume** of 512cm³?

_____ × _____ × _____   /1

29. What is the width of a cuboid with a volume of 396cm³, a height of 11cm and a length of 9cm?

_____   /1

30. What are the two largest **prime numbers** below 100 whose sum is 186?

_____ and _____   /1

31. Draw the **reflection** on the second grid.   /1

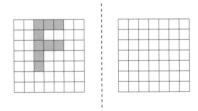

32–35. List the common **factors** for each of these sets of numbers.

16, 40 and 52 → _____   24, 30 and 42 → _____

20, 32 and 60 → _____   40, 80 and 120 → _____   /4

36–38. (290 – 140) × 4 = _____   500 – (200 × 2) = _____   (12 + 6) ÷ (27 ÷ 3) = _____   /3

Look at the table.

Pounds (£)	2	4	8	10
Euros (€)	2.4	4.8	9.6	12.0

39–40. Plot the amounts given in the table and draw a line to join the points. Then work out the answers to questions 41–46 using the **conversion** graph you have drawn.

/2

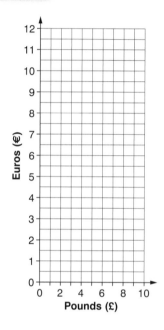

41. How many euros would you receive for £1? _____

42. How many euros would you receive for £9.50? _____

43. How many pounds would you receive for 5 euros? _____

44. How many pounds would you receive for 10 euros? _____

45. How many euros would you receive for £500? _____

46. How many pounds would you receive for 500 euros? _____

/6

Use these numbers to answer the questions.

12.635   12.569   12.467   12.684   12.235

47. ▦ What is the answer if you subtract the smallest number from the biggest number? _____

48. ⊞ Which two numbers have a **difference** of 0.049? _____

49. ⊞ Which number is 0.232 less than 12.467? _____

50. ⊞ Which number is 0.115 less than the greatest number? _____

/4

/50

PAPER 14

Answer these.

1. If a number when rounded to one decimal place equals 27.7, circle the number it could have been before being rounded.

   26.75   26.64   26.608   27.79   27.65

/1

2. If a number when rounded to three decimal places equals 0.873, circle the number it could have been before being rounded.

   0.8735   0.8731   0.8724   0.8739   0.8635

/1

3–6. Write the lowest **multiples** of these pairs of numbers.

   4 and 7 _____   9 and 12 _____   4 and 6 _____   6 and 9 _____

/4

Write the length of time between these pairs of times.

7. 16 minutes to 8 in the morning until 5 minutes to 12 noon _____

8. 8 minutes past 11 in the morning until 10 minutes past 4 in the afternoon _____

9. 9.39am until 3.25pm _____

10. 10.53pm until 2.31am _____

/4

Work out these sums.

11.

 ÷ 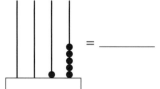 = _____

12.

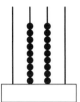 ÷ 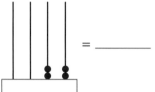 = _____

/2

Work out the missing numbers.

13.   4 6 5 ☐
        – 1 8 9 3
        ─────────────
        ☐ 7 5 9

14.   ☐ 3 2 4
        – 3 5 5 ☐
        ─────────────
        4 7 6 8

15.   2 3 0 0
        – ☐ 4 5 9
        ─────────────
        8 4 ☐

16.   7 ☐ 5 1
        – 6 2 ☐ 8
        ─────────────
        1 1 0 3

/4

Solve these problems.

17. In cricket, Andrew has an average of 67 runs per game in the 25 games he has played in.

To reach an average of at least 70 runs per game by the time he has played 30 games, how many runs on average must he score per game in the remaining 5 games? _____

/1

18. Tickets for the concert cost £35 for an adult and £20 for a child. It costs £10 for a programme. 150 adults and 60 children go to the concert and 80% of adults buy a programme.

How much money is spent on tickets and programmes for the concert? _____

/1

19. Car A's petrol tank holds 60 litres of petrol and Car B's tank holds 40 litres of petrol.

If Car A travels at 9km per litre and Car B travels at 7km per litre, which car will travel furthest on 1 tank of petrol? _____

/1

In a sponsored walk the distance Lennox walks is measured every five minutes. The table shows the distances he walked. Plot these figures on the graph and answer the questions.

Time (minutes)	0	5	10	15	20
Distance (metres)	0	400	800	1200	1600

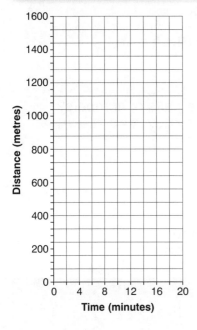

20. How far had Lennox walked after 6 minutes? _____

21. How far had he walked after 12 minutes? _____

22. How long does it take for Lennox to walk 200 metres? _____

23. How long does it take for Lennox to walk 1300 metres? _____ /4

Answer these.

24. Staton Ice Hockey team has won 3 games to every game lost. This season they have played 20 games.

How many games have they won? _____ /1

25. On the fruit and vegetable stall in the market, there are 121 apples and the **proportion** of red apples to green apples is 6 : 5.

How many red apples are there? _____   /1

26. A rock climber is $\frac{3}{7}$ of the way up a 91m rock face.

How far has she climbed? _____   /1

27–31. Draw brackets to make each number sentence true.

$$45 - 15 + 18 = 48 \qquad 10 \times 6 + 2 = 80 \qquad 5 + 50 \div 5 = 11$$

$$28 - 14 \times 2 = 28 \qquad 36 \div 6 + 3 = 4$$ /5

What are the mid points between each of these pairs of numbers?

32. 26.46 ☐ 26.52

33. 89.73 ☐ 89.93

34. 199.99 ☐ 200.11   /3

Calculate the **perimeter** and **area** of these shapes.

35.

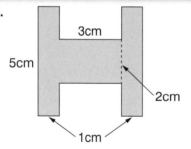

3cm

5cm

2cm

1cm

36.

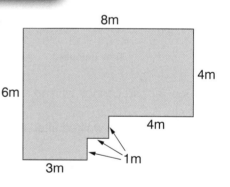

8m

4m

6m

4m

3m

1m

Perimeter = _____ Area = _____   Perimeter = _____ Area = _____   /2

Write < or > between each pair of amounts.

37. $\frac{2}{7}$ of 49 ☐ $\frac{4}{9}$ of 36

38. $\frac{7}{8}$ of 16 ☐ $\frac{1}{4}$ of 44

39. $\frac{2}{5}$ of 15 ☐ $\frac{1}{7}$ of 28

40. $\frac{3}{11}$ of 77 ☐ $\frac{6}{7}$ of 28

41. $\frac{7}{9}$ of 45 ☐ $\frac{3}{4}$ of 48

42. $\frac{1}{8}$ of 64 ☐ $\frac{3}{8}$ of 16   /6

A bag contains a number of vowels. There are six As, eight Es, four Is, four Os and two Us. Answer the questions as fractions in their lowest terms.

43. What is the **probability** of taking out an E? _____

44. What is the probability of taking out an A? _____

45. What is the probability of taking out a vowel? _____

46. What is the probability of taking out a consonant? _____   /4

This graph shows the number of different types of DVDs owned by a family.

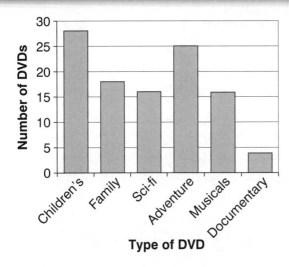

47. What is the most popular type of DVD? _____

48. The family has seven less of one type of DVD than Adventure.

Which type? _____

49. What is the **difference** in number between the type of DVDs the family has most of compared with the type of DVD they have least of? _____

50. How many DVDs does the family have in total? _____   /4

/50

PAPER 15

Count in these steps. Write in the missing numbers.

1. Count back in 1000s ➔ 92 196 _____ _____ _____ 88 196

2. Count on in 1000s ➔ 29 300 _____ _____ _____ 33 300

3. Count back in 10 000s ➔ 91 023 _____ _____ _____ 51 023

4. Count on in 10 000s ➔ 62 956 _____ _____ _____ 102 956   /4

Work out the **equivalent** distances in km to the nearest 10km (1 mile = 1.6 kilometres).

5. Hull to Leeds = 60 miles _____km

6. Edinburgh to Glasgow = 52 miles _____km

7. Leicester to Norwich = 131 miles _____km

8. Milton Keynes to Bristol = 109 miles _____km   /4

Find the missing numbers.

9. $312 - \boxed{} = 500 \div 25$ **10.** $724 + \boxed{} = 33 \times 25$

11. $960 \div 40 = \boxed{} \times 12$ **12.** $26 \times 30 = \boxed{} \div 2$ /4

Find these amounts.

13. Ollie spends $\frac{4}{9}$ of the £279 in his bank account.

How much did he spend? _____

14. Nabeel reads $\frac{3}{7}$ of the 315 pages in his book during the holidays.

How many pages did he read? _____

15. Charlotte is walking from home to school and she is $\frac{3}{8}$ of the way there. The distance from home to school is 600m.

How much further to the school? _____

16. The boat's cargo weighs 498kg. $\frac{5}{6}$ of the cargo is unloaded at the port.

How much is unloaded? _____   /4

What is the order of **rotational symmetry** of these shapes?

17.

Square

18.

Rectangle

19.

Parallelogram

20.

Trapezium

21.

Kite

_____   _____   _____   _____   _____   /5

Complete this table.

22–30.

	Round to the nearest 100	Round to the nearest 1000	Round to the nearest 10000
7632			
86523			
31989			

/9

Work out the missing angles.

31–34.

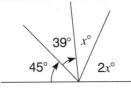   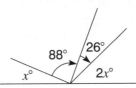

angle x = _____   angle $2x$ = _____   angle x = _____   angle $2x$ = _____   /4

Answer these.

35. $21765 + 45 + 389 + 2568 =$ _____   **36.** $15603 + 256 + 3610 + 12 =$ _____

37. $12306 - 4537 =$ _____   **38.** $15000 - 5236 =$ _____   /4

39–41. Find the value of the following **expressions** if $x = 12$.

$3x - (35 - x) = \boxed{}$ $(2x + 7) - 15 = \boxed{}$ $3x - (2x - 8) = \boxed{}$ /3

This graph shows how many children's birthdays fall in each month.

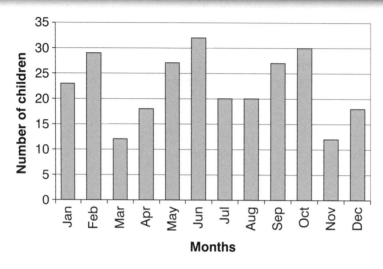

42. Which three months have most birthdays? _____

43. Which two months have fewest birthdays? _____

44. How many months have 20 birthdays or fewer? _____

45. How many birthdays are there in the first six months of the year? _____   /4

The numbers 1 to 10 are put into a bag by a teacher
and children are invited to take a number out.

46. What is the **probability** that a child pulls an even number from the bag? _____

47. What is the probability that a child pulls out a number that is in the 3 times tables? _____

48. What is the probability that a child pulls out a number that is in the 5 times tables? _____

49. What is the probability that a child pulls out a 2-**digit** number? _____

50. What is the probability that a child pulls out a **prime number**? _____   /5

/50

PAPER 16

Write the missing numbers in each of these.

1. ☐ × 20 = 56

2. 4.3 × ☐ = 86

3. ☐ × 200 = 740

4. 104 ÷ ☐ = 5.2

5. ☐ ÷ 200 = 32.24

6. 648 ÷ ☐ = 3.24

/6

Work out the value of each letter.

7. $3y - 18 = 6$ $y =$ _____

8. $19 + 5z = 24$ $z =$ _____

9. $27 - 3e = -9$ $e =$ _____

10. $6h - 4 = -16$ $h =$ _____

/4

Answer these.

11. At the local garden centre there are 240 plants placed in 24 rows. 50% more plants are delivered and placed on the rows.

How many plants are now in each row? _____

/1

12. Cans of drink are delivered to a sporting event. Each can is 330ml in size and 96 cans are delivered. $\frac{1}{3}$ of the cans are cola.

How many litres of cola are there? _____

/1

13–15. What is the order of **rotational symmetry** of these shapes?

Equilateral triangle _____   **Isosceles triangle** _____   Scalene triangle _____   /3

16–21. In a survey in the local town, adults and children were asked which they preferred for a fast food meal – pizza or fish and chips. 213 people were asked and 69 children preferred pizza. Use this information to complete the table.

	Pizza	Fish and chips	Total
Adults		78	
Children			111
Total			213

/6

Look at the grid.

22. What are the **coordinates** of **vertex** A? (_____ , _____)

/1

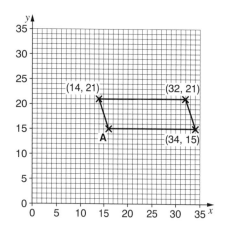

23. Draw the two diagonals on the parallelogram. What are the coordinates for the point where the diagonals cross? (_____ , _____)

/1

Work out the **equivalent** distances (1 mile = 1.6 kilometres).

24. ⊞ Coventry to Gloucester = 120km _____ miles

25. ⊞ Stoke to Derby = 60km _____ miles

26. ⊞ York to Manchester = 110km _____ miles

27. ⊞ Exeter to Taunton = 50km _____ miles

/4

Calculate these sums.

28. Matchboxes have these dimensions – 5cm × 3cm × 1cm. They are placed in a box with these dimensions – 10cm × 6cm × 4cm.

    How many matchboxes can be placed in the bigger box? _____   /1

29. A boat is sailing from London to New York, a distance of 3500 miles. The boat is 40% of the way to New York.

    How many miles does the boat still have to travel? _____   /1

30. A plane is flying from Sydney to London, a distance of 10 600 miles. It is 70% of the way there.

    How far has it gone? _____   /1

31. Jamie wants to fly from London to Vancouver, a distance of 4800 miles.

    If he stops in Montreal, which is 3200 miles from
    London, what **percentage** of the journey will he have done? _____   /1

32. Sarah is going to fly to Hong Kong from London, a distance of 6000 miles. To break up the journey she is looking to stop after about 60% of the journey.

    If she does, how far will she have travelled? _____   /1

This graph shows the amount of money made in a shop sale over seven days.

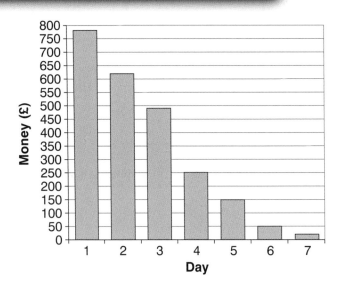

33. How much money was made in the first two days? _____

34. On which day did the shop's total takings reach £2000? _____

35. On which two days did the shop make a total of £400? _____ /3

Work out the mystery number for each of these statements.

36. When I divide a number by 3, and then add 125, the answer is 165. _____

37. When I multiply a number by 6, and then subtract 60, the answer is 240. _____

38. When I square a number, and then divide by 20, the answer is 5. _____

39. When I multiply a number by 4 and then take its **square root**, the answer is 6. _____ /4

Complete these sentences by writing the most sensible measurement from the list.

| 150 metres | 5ml | 40km | 1kg | 400g | 2 litres |

40. A can of baked beans weighs _____.

41. She walked _____ to the shops.

42. He took _____ of cough mixture.

43. She ran just over _____ in the marathon.

44. A hard-backed book weighs _____.

45. A tub of ice cream holds _____.

/6

Answer these.

46–49. Write in the missing **digits**.

$$142 \boxed{} \div 25 = \boxed{} 7 \qquad 396 \boxed{} \div 32 = 12 \boxed{}$$

/4

50. $\sqrt{3^2 + 4^2} =$ _____

/1

/50

PAPER 17

Answer these.

1. Circle the **square numbers**.

5   12   16   40   81   104   121

/1

2–10. Complete this table by rounding the population numbers.

	Round to the nearest 100	Round to the nearest 1000	Round to the nearest 10000
Brigfield 34293			
Nottibury 49584			
Liverton 69017			

/9

11–14. Work out the angles marked in the parallelogram and rhombus.

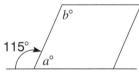

115°

Parallelogram

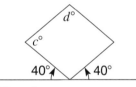

40°   40°

Rhombus

$a°$ = _____ $b°$ = _____ $c°$ = _____ $d°$ = _____

/4

15–17. Join the pairs of prices that total £500.

£318.42   £111.58

£381.24   £181.58

£388.42   £118.76

/3

This table shows the heights of the world's tallest mountains. Look at the table and answer these questions.

Mountain	Height (metres)
Everest	8850
K2	8612
Kanchenjunga	8586
Lhotse 1	8501
Makalu 1	8462
Cho Oyu	8201

18. How much higher is Everest than Cho Oyu? _____

19. Which mountain is 111 metres smaller than K2? _____

20. Which mountain is 124 metres taller than Makalu 1? _____

21. If a mountaineer was keeping a record of her climbs, how many metres would she have recorded if she got to the top of the world's three tallest mountains?

_____

22. If a climber is 95% of the way up Everest, how much further has he left to climb?

_____

23. Mount Everest is growing in height at about 6cm per year. How tall will it be in 100 years?

_____

/6

Answer these.

24. $((5 \times 12) \times (20 \div 10)) \div 12 =$ _____   25. $((8 + (7 \times 2)) \div 11 =$ _____

/2

26. 35 cakes in each of 7 rows. How many cakes? _____

27. 56 books on each of 9 shelves. How many books? _____

28. 56 panes of glass on each level of an 8 level building. How many panes of glass? _____

/3

29–33. What fraction of £500 is each of these numbers?

£250 ⬚/⬚   £100 ⬚/⬚   £400 ⬚/⬚

£50 ⬚/⬚   £75 ⬚/⬚

/5

34–36. What is the **mean**, **median** and **mode** of these sprint times of a group of runners?

9.9   9.81   9.69   9.9   10.01   9.79   9.85

▦ Mean = _____   Median = _____   Mode = _____

/3

37. Michael has a toy car which is 1 : 75 the size of the real car. His toy car is 5.6cm long.

What is the length of the real car? _____

/1

38–40. Write the missing numbers in these **sequences**.

		26	52	104		
		30	90	270		
		16	64	256		

/3

Look at the kite in the grid.

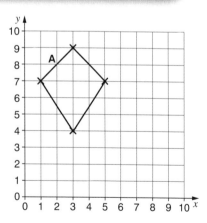

41. What are the **coordinates** of kite A?

_____

42. Draw kite B at the following coordinates: (7, 3), (5, 6), (7, 8) and (9, 6).

43. Is kite B a **translation**, **rotation** or **reflection** of kite A? _____ /3

Tick true or false for each of these statements.

44. An **isosceles triangle** has three lines of **symmetry**. True ☐ False ☐

45. Semi-circles have **infinite** lines of symmetry. True ☐ False ☐

46. A regular pentagon has five lines of symmetry. True ☐ False ☐

47. A trapezium has one pair of **parallel** sides. True ☐ False ☐

48. A rhombus has all sides of equal length. True ☐ False ☐ /5

Answer these.

49. What is the **area** of a square patio with a **perimeter** of 28m? _____

50. ▦ What is the perimeter of a square room with an area of 12.25m²? _____ /2

/50

adjacent	two sides of a shape that are joined at a vertex
approximate	a 'rough' answer – near to the real answer
area	the area of a shape is the amount of surface it covers
clockwise	turning in this direction
conversion	changing from one unit of measurement to another
coordinate	number that shows the exact position of something on a grid
difference	the difference between two numbers is the amount by which one number is greater or smaller than the other. Example: the difference between 18 and 21 is 3
digit	there are 10 digits **0 1 2 3 4 5 6 7 8** and **9** that make all the numbers we use
edge	where two faces of a solid shape meet edge→
equation	a mathematical statement which always includes an equals sign and says that two things are the same. An algebraic equation uses letters or symbols instead of numbers, e.g. $x + 3 = 7$ (if $x + 3$ is equal to 7, x must be 4)
equivalent	two numbers or measures are equivalent if they are the same or equal
estimate	a good guess
expression	when letters are used to represent numbers in an equation
factor	a number that will divide exactly into other numbers. Example: 5 is a factor of 20
infinite	greater than any imaginable number
isosceles triangle	a triangle which has two sides of the same length and two angles of the same size
mean	the total divided by the number of items. Example: the mean of 3, 1, 6 and 2 is $(3 + 1 + 6 + 2) \div 4 = 3$
median	the middle number in an ordered list. Example: 3, 8, 11, 15, 16 – the median number is 11
mode	the most common number in a list. Example: 2, 6, 4, 2, 5, 5, 2 – the mode is 2
multiple	a number made by multiplying together two other numbers
negative number	a number less than zero on the number line
net	the net of a 3-D shape is what it looks like when it is opened out flat
parallel	lines that are always the same distance apart and will never meet – they also point in the same direction
percentage	a fraction out of 100, shown with a % sign
perimeter	the outer edge of a shape
prime number	only has two factors, 1 and itself. Example: 23 is a prime number because it can only be divided exactly by 1 and 23

probability	the likelihood that an event will occur shown as a fraction, percentage or decimal. Example: $\frac{1}{2}$, 50% or 0.5
product	the result of multiplying two or more numbers
proportion	this is the same as finding the fraction of the whole amount. Example: the proportion of black cubes is 3 out of 5 or $\frac{3}{5}$
protractor	a tool for measuring angles
range	the difference between the highest and lowest values of a set of data
ratio	this compares one amount with another. Example: the ratio of red cubes to blue cubes is 3:2
reflection	the mirror image of an original figure
remainder	if a number cannot be divided exactly by another number, there is a whole number amount left over, called a remainder
rotation	turning a shape or figure around a fixed point
rotational symmetry	when an object looks the same after a certain amount of rotation
sequence	a list of numbers which usually have a pattern. They are often numbers written in order
square number	numbers multiplied by themselves make square numbers. Example: $4 \times 4 = 16$. The first five square numbers are 1, 4, 9, 16 and 25
square root	the opposite of a square number. Example: square root of 25 = 5
symmetry (symmetrical)	when two halves of a shape or pattern are identical
translation	the movement of a figure or shape in a straight line where no rotation occurs
triangular-based pyramid/tetrahedron	a three-dimensional shape consisting of four triangular faces
vertex (plural – vertices)	a corner or point where lines meet but do not cross. Example: a square has four corners and each is called a vertex
volume	the size of or room inside a 3-D shape

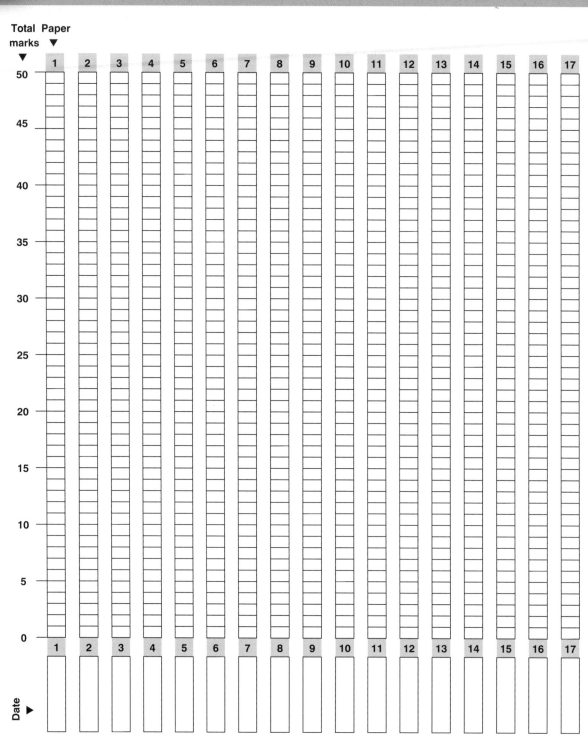

Total Paper
marks ▼
▼

Date ▶

Now colour in your score!